BABY'S FIRST BOOK

illustrated by CLARE BEATON

Barefoot Books
Celebrating Art and Story

CONTENTS

Once I caught a fish alive
Fabulous fish
All the birds of the air
Creepy crawlies
A hive for a honey bee
Weather
High in the sky
Across the waves
On the move
The elephant
My first letters
My first numbers
My first shapes
Teddy bear

ROUND THE GARDEN

Round and round the garden

Like a teddy bear;

One step, two steps,

Tickle you under there!

Run your index finger around the baby's palm, then jump
the fingers up the arm and tickle under the chin.

BAA BAA BLACK SHEEP

Baa baa black sheep,
Have you any wool?
Yes sir, yes sir,
Three bags full.

One for the master,
One for the dame;
One for the little boy
Who lives down the lane.

MY SUMMER CLOTHES

MY WINTER CLOTHES

MY TOY CHEST

I HAD A LITTLE ENGINE

I had a little engine,
But it wouldn't go;
I had to push and push and push,
But still it wouldn't go.

I had a little motor car,
But it wouldn't go;
I had to wind and wind
　　　　　　and wind,
But still it wouldn't go.

I had a little aeroplane,
My aeroplane could fly;
I jumped right in, away I flew,
Right into the sky.

In the first verse, pretend to push hard; in the second verse, pretend to wind the handle; in the third verse, run round the room with your arms stretched out.

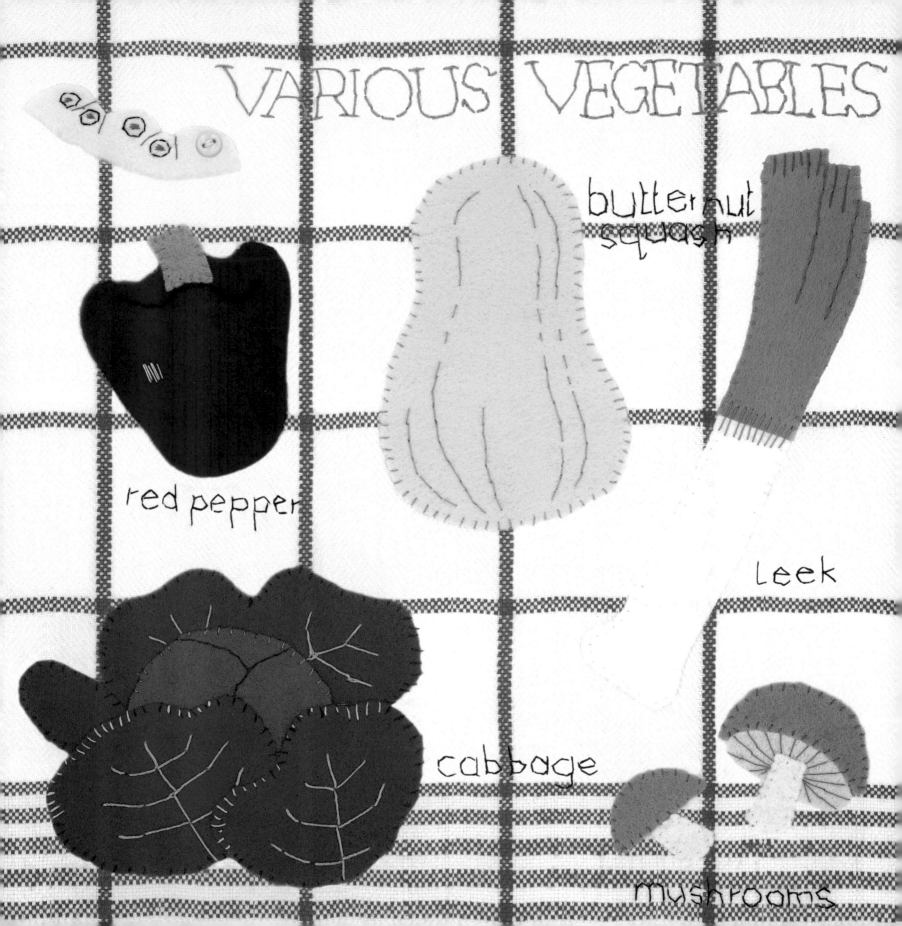

VARIOUS VEGETABLES

butternut squash

red pepper

Leek

cabbage

mushrooms

carrots

broccoli

cauliflower

peas

onion

otatoes

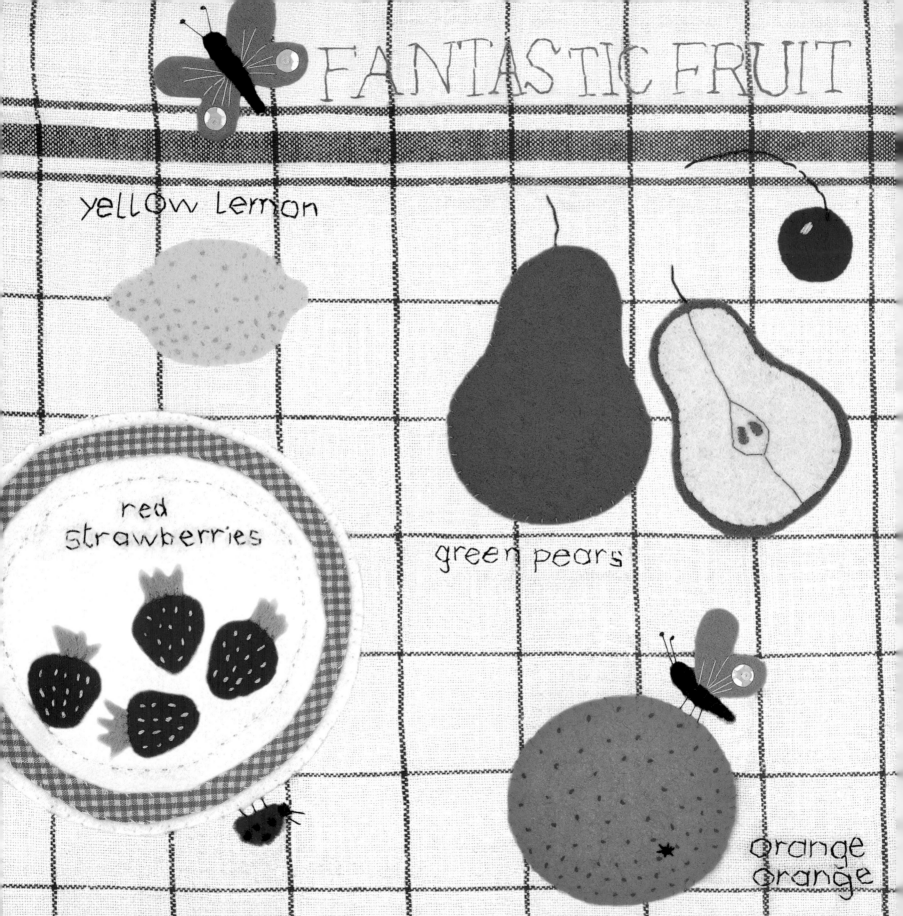

FANTASTIC FRUIT

yellow lemon

green pears

red strawberries

orange orange

purple grapes

red cherries

yellow banana

pink watermelon

red apple

TEDDY BEAR'S PICNIC

PAT-A-CAKE

Pat-a-cake, pat-a-cake,

Baker's man,

Bake me a cake

As fast as you can.

Pat it and prick it

And mark it with B,

And put it in the oven

For Baby and me.

*Sit opposite your baby and clap hands, first clapping right hands together,
then left hands together, then both hands together.*

ANIMALS WITH BIG TEETH

walrus

donkey

horse

rabbit

tiger

crocodile

ANIMALS WITH TAILS

squirrel

monkey

beaver

raccoon

leopard

big

rabbit

elephant

THIS LITTLE PIGGY

This little piggy went to market,

This little piggy stayed at home,

This little piggy had roast beef,

This little piggy had none,

And this little piggy cried,

wee-wee-wee-wee-wee,

All the way home.

Point to each toe in turn, starting with the big one;
on the last line, tickle the baby's foot.

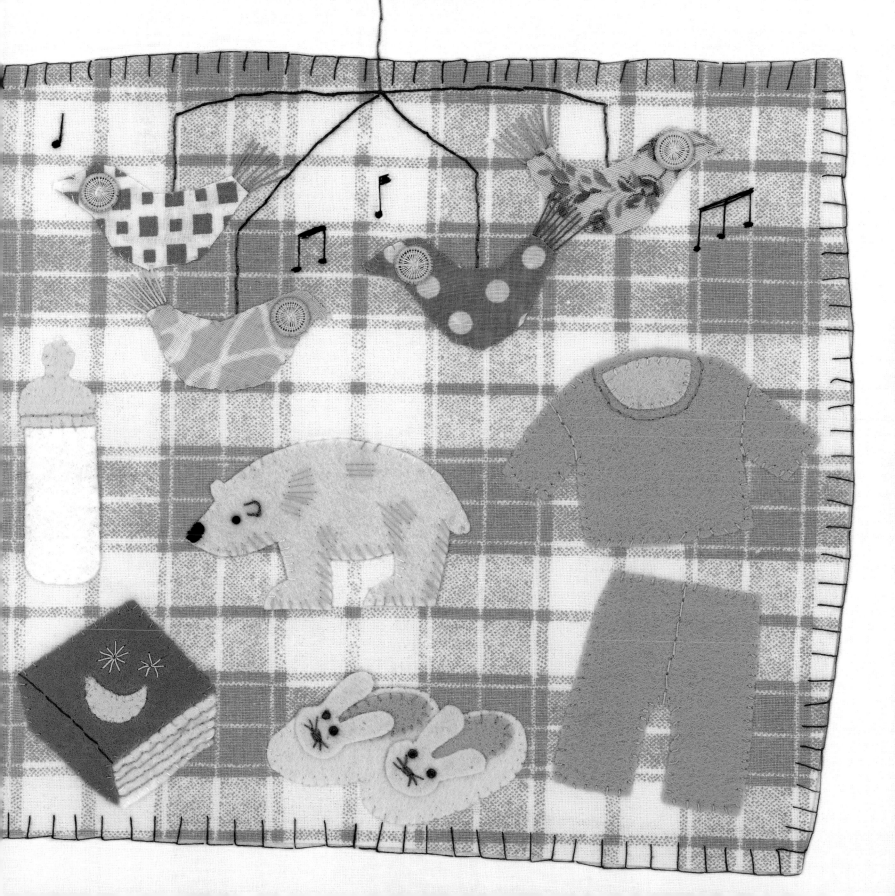

BATHTIME

ONCE I CAUGHT A FISH ALIVE

One, two, three, four, five,

Once I caught a fish alive.

Six, seven, eight, nine, ten,

Then I let it go again.

Why did you let it go?

Because it bit my finger so!

Which finger did it bite?

This little finger on my right.

Count on your fingers; wriggle your hand like a fish; count on your fingers; pretend to throw the fish back; shake hand violently; hold up little finger of right hand.

FABULOUS FISH

ALL THE BIRDS OF
THE AIR

CREEPY CRAWLIES

A hive for a honey bee,

A kennel for a dog;

A hutch for a rabbit,

And a pond for a frog;

A stable for a donkey,   A hole for a mouse . . .

But I would like a caravan
For my special house!

Sunny

Rainy

Snowy

Windy

HIGH IN THE SKY

ACROSS THE WAVES

ON THE MOVE

THE ELEPHANT

An elephant goes like this and that.

He's terribly big and he's terribly fat.

He has no fingers,

He has no toes,

But goodness gracious, what a nose!

Touch your knees and then stretch your arms above your head.
Open your arms wide, then wiggle your fingers and touch your toes.
Finally, stretch one arm out like a trunk.

MY FIRST LETTERS

A B C D
E F G H I
J K L M

MY FIRST NUMBERS

1
2
3
7
8

MY FIRST SHAPES

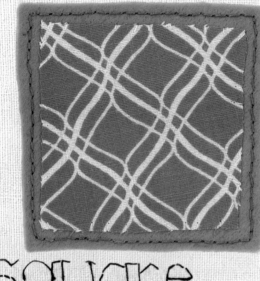

square

oval

heart

star

diamond

crescent

circle

rectangle

triangle

TEDDY BEAR

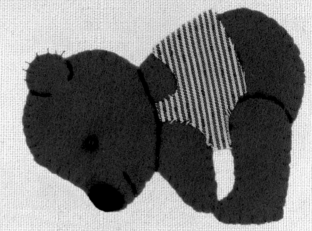

Teddy bear, teddy bear,
touch your toes.

Teddy bear, teddy bear,
touch your nose.

Teddy bear, teddy bear,
touch the ground.

Teddy bear, teddy bear, turn around.

Teddy bear, teddy bear,
climb the stairs.

Teddy bear, teddy bear,
say your prayers.

Teddy bear, teddy bear,
turn off the light.

Teddy bear, teddy bear,
say goodnight!

Follow the actions, then blow a big kiss on 'Goodnight!'

Clare Beaton is an award-winning children's writer and illustrator who lives and works in North London. Clare has gained international recognition for her distinctive collages: she hand sews her illustrations using felt, vintage fabrics, buttons and sequins — whatever she can find that can be reused and given a new life. For more information on Clare's many beautiful picture books, visit www.barefootbooks.com

For Baby Jenkins — C. B.

Barefoot Books, 124 Walcot Street, Bath, BA1 5BG

Illustrations copyright © 2008 by Clare Beaton
The moral right of Clare Beaton to be identified as the illustrator of this work has been asserted

First published in Great Britain by Barefoot Books, Ltd in 2008

This book has been printed on 100% acid-free paper. Graphic design by Barefoot Books, Bath
Reproduction by Bright Arts, Singapore. Printed and bound in Singapore by Tien Wah Press Pte Ltd

This book was typeset in Soupbone and Stone Informal
The illustrations were prepared in antique fabrics and felt with buttons, beads and assorted bric-a-brac
Hardback ISBN 978-1-84686-142-0

British Cataloguing-in-Publication Data:
a catalogue record for this book is available from the British Library

1 3 5 7 9 8 6 4 2

Barefoot Books
Celebrating Art and Story

At Barefoot Books, we celebrate art and story that opens
the hearts and minds of children from all walks of life, inspiring
them to read deeper, search further, and explore their own creative gifts.
Taking our inspiration from many different cultures, we focus on themes that
encourage independence of spirit, enthusiasm for learning, and sharing of
the world's diversity. Interactive, playful and beautiful, our products
combine the best of the present with the best of the past to
educate our children as the caretakers of tomorrow.

Live Barefoot!
Join us at www.barefootbooks.com